Illustrations by
MEGAMUNDEN

Text and guidance by
DIANA MCMAHON COLLIS

LAURENCE KING PUBLISHING

Laurence King Publishing Ltd.
361–373 City Road
London EC1V 1LR
United Kingdom
www.laurenceking.com

ISBN: 978-1-78627-809-8

Text by Diana McMahon Collis
© 2018, 2020 Laurence King Publishing Ltd.
Illustrations © 2018, 2020 MEGAMUNDEN, Oliver Munden
Design by Renata Latipova

Selected text extracted from *Tattoo Tarot* and *Tattoo Tarot Journal*,
© 2018, 2020 Laurence King Publishing Ltd.

Printed in China

MEGAMUNDEN would like to thank his loved ones for all the support
given during the production of this book in such unusual times.

Special thanks to Vanessa Munden & Hayley Barden for food and water,
to David and Joshua Munden and a big shout-out to Ethan Barden.

Lockdown crew 2020.

Laurence King Publishing is committed to ethical and sustainable book
production. We are proud participants in The Book Chain Project ®
bookchainproject.com

X
THE WHEEL
OF FORTUNE

Key Meanings
Cycles of life. Destiny. Evolution. Advancement. Success. Manifestation. Unexpected events. Sudden luck. Ups and downs. One person's loss, another's gain.

Wisdom
Are you experiencing an upward surge of energy and fortunes, or do you feel that you're taking a downward turn? Be ready to ride that wave or weather the storm – just remember, each stage is temporary. When you are succeeding, watch out for a snake in the grass; when you're not, hold tight and fix your sights on the horizon.

Colour Notes
A fifteenth-century Milanese deck features the Wheel of Fortune in gold, green and light and dark shades of blue.

COLOUR
IN TAROT

The earliest known examples of tarot cards were commissioned by fifteenth-century Italy's nobility and were inspired, in part, by illuminated Egyptian playing cards, which were hand painted and decorated with hammered gold leaf. Tarot's popularity grew slowly in Europe – notably Italy, Germany, France, Belgium and Switzerland – with early producers using woodblocks, labour-intensive engraving and hand-tinting, combining three or four colours only. In later centuries, use of copper moulds, stencilling, modern printing and lithography simplified and improved production processes, bringing tarot to a mass audience and encompassing a broader colour palette. From the twentieth century, influence from various esoteric schools modified original designs, but tarot's decorative roots continue to underpin card meanings, with colour playing a significant role.

0

THE FOOL

Key Meanings

The seeker. Innocence. Naivety. Courage. Humour. Living in the now. Journey's outset. Burst of energy. Everything open, all paths available. Madness. Folly. Instability.

Wisdom

The Fool means you are setting out on a fresh venture and moving into uncharted territory. Travel light and let little hold you back. Allow yourself to explore, revel in your freedom and enjoy the sense of adventure. Stop and take in the view, unimpeded by agendas or complex commitments. If you do meet with dark clouds, remember that they will pass. Know that there is an advantage to every situation.

Colour Notes

Historically, the Fool was often depicted in a Harlequin costume, in various shades of red, green, yellow, blue, purple, white and black.

I
THE
MAGICIAN

Key Meanings
The juggler. The trickster. Power. Divine connection and inspiration. Skill, talent. Enterprise and initiative. Willpower. Mastery. Self-control. Diplomacy. Subtlety. Dexterity.

Wisdom
The Magician shows you can have it all if you trust yourself. You may have the gift of the gab or be very physically able. Where you lack skill or experience, you will easily find ways to improve. You may even have the Midas touch, helping to increase wealth. You also have the ability to connect with others, mentally and emotionally, which means you hold all the aces. But remember, the onus is on you to use your talents for the highest good, with karma in play.

Colour Notes
Part cavalier, part jester, a classic French rendition offers a costume in striking divisions of red, blue and yellow.

II
THE HIGH PRIESTESS

Key Meanings
Moon goddess. Deep knowledge. Intuition. Foresight. Intelligence. Enlightenment. Wisdom. Inspiration. Mystery. Gnosis. Divination. Prophecy. Sanctuary.

Wisdom
The High Priestess means it's time to pay heed to the inner voice to receive greater insight and peace. The wisdom of third-eye knowledge and alignment of the heart can, together, show the best way forward. You may be more psychic than usual – seeing all, hearing all – but unable to put it into words. Observe, listen and relax. Sometimes the less said, the better.

Colour Notes
In eighteenth- and nineteenth-century decks, the Priestess has appeared as the 'Papess', wearing a red, gold-trimmed chasuble.

III

THE EMPRESS

Key Meanings
The queen. Feminine power. Matriarch. Mother. Fertility.
Pleasure. Luxury. Beauty. Success. Initiative. Evolution.
Movement. Marriage. Wealth.

Wisdom
The Empress is the power behind the throne and sometimes
the symbolic figurehead. Mother, or crone with maternal
and matriarchal tendencies, she has a charmed life but also
holds special responsibilities. Are you in a position to care for
other people? Do you need to balance this with taking care
of yourself? When you feel stuck, try not to force creativity –
it will return.

Colour Notes
Over the centuries, the Empress's robe has often been coloured
in green, red or white with red pomegranates.

IV
THE EMPEROR

Key Meanings
The king. Male power. Authority. Leadership. Proficiency. Wealth. Stability. Perseverance. Endurance. Realisation. Being effective. Logic. Experience.

Wisdom
The Emperor has the power to confidently lead others, whatever resistance may be met. He manages to sustain a situation or garner faith, respect and following from others. Sometimes we can struggle with stepping up to a position of authority. Do what you can. Where you lack knowledge or strength, seek help or information. Find someone you look up to and work to develop similar qualities to them.

Colour Notes
Red – associated with activity, passion and divine love – has often featured, sometimes alongside dark blue, which is linked with receptivity.

V
THE
HIEROPHANT

Key Meanings
Tradition. Convention. Ritual. Symbolism. Ceremony. Religion. Religious practices. Morality. Social approval. Instruction. Philosophy. Universal law. Mercy. Goodness. Forgiveness. Humility. Vulnerability.

Wisdom
The Hierophant urges that now is the time to seek the right way to do things and follow protocol. Find instruction in established practices. Follow a spiritual path, which may have traditions and rituals attached, or establish and adhere to your own moral code. A deeper understanding of human nature and errors may be required. Be prepared to offer or seek forgiveness, where appropriate.

Colour Notes
A blue and red combination dominated eighteenth- and nineteenth-century colouring; a mid-twentieth-century deck emphasised red and white.

VI
THE LOVERS

Key Meanings
Love. Attraction. Virtue. Compatibility. Harmony. Triumph over trials. Choice. Intuitive decisions. Union. Entanglement. Enmeshment. Infidelity. Moral lapse. Vice. Separation.

Wisdom
The Lovers invites you to tune into the needs of the heart, but also to use your head to recognise where your actions could hurt someone. A passionate, possibly steamy situation threatens to absorb all your attention. Take stock of what you are getting into; is this love a lucky horseshoe or does it lead you into a ring of fire?

Colour Notes
Ancient tarots featured a love triangle of three humans, clothed in red and black – linked to hidden affairs.

VII
THE CHARIOT

Key Meanings
Journey. Ordeal. Obstacle. Competition. High stakes. Ambition. Discipline. Conquest. Victory. Greatness. Reason triumphs. The work of the will. Right action prevails.

Wisdom
The Chariot encourages you to think on your feet and plan as you go. To set your sights firmly on winning, or on getting to the end of something. You can pick the pieces up later, if needed. Even in the midst of dizzying ambition, try to keep steady and stay on track, though calm may feel out of reach at the moment. Be sure to balance conflicting forces.

Colour Notes
Red, blue and yellow were often featured in ancient tarot Chariot depictions, emphasising a combination of activity, intuition and intelligence.

VIII

JUSTICE

Key Meanings

Balance. Equilibrium. Equality. Symmetry. Harmony. Integrity. Honour. Fairness. Neutrality. Moderation. Attraction and repulsion polarity. Vindication.

Wisdom

The Justice card is about being poised and steady, accessing inner alignment and calm. Pay attention to what feels right and act on that basis. Do not take sides. Maintain equanimity. Recognise injustice, or where life is out of balance. Where does it make sense to compromise? Can you meet someone halfway? But recognise when you need to hold your ground.

Colour Notes

Combinations of red, blue and green featured historically; Justice's scales tended to be golden, probably signifying brass apothecary scales.

IX
THE HERMIT

Key Meaning
The seeker. Sage. Wisdom and inspiration from above or within. Vigilance. Withdrawal. Contemplation. Discretion. Safety. Protection. Seeking truth and justice. Spiritual quest. Understanding.

Wisdom
The Hermit presents an opportunity to go underground or stay under the covers. It's time to focus on yourself and your inner world. Trust your own wisdom and judgement. Play your cards close to your chest. Your path ahead may not be immediately clear, so take gradual steps. Collect your thoughts. Allow a night's sleep, ideally, before responding to someone.

Colour Notes
The Hermit's cloak was traditionally a deep blue; its lining, in a Parisian deck from 1650, was brown and gold.

XI

STRENGTH

Key Meanings
Resilience. Strength of mind. Courage. Resolve. Confidence. Integrity. Moral victory. Spiritual rectitude. Endurance. Energy. Action. Vitality. Power. Force.

Wisdom
The Strength card can mean you are grappling with inner demons. It can also be about levelling with someone who has behaved badly. The task ahead may seem bigger than you are, but keep your nerve and trust that you'll find a way forward. Believe in yourself, you have strengths that can combat tough situations in unexpected ways. Remember, someone may be all talk, or their bark may be worse than their bite.

Colour Notes
In an ancient Italian deck, the lion is golden; the main figure is robed in red and blue.

XII

THE HANGED MAN

Key Meanings
Delay. Sacrifices. Reversals. Pending decisions. Review. Readjustment. Abandonment. Rejection. Betrayal. Falseness. Restrained or bound. Trials. Caution. Being in limbo.

Wisdom
If in doubt, pause. The Hanged Man is about seeing the world from a different perspective. Sometimes we don't have the solution to hand – it's fine to put something on hold until the right action becomes clearer. A situation may not go to plan. Consider that a rejection may also be a form of protection.

Colour Notes
In a mid-seventeenth-century French version, the man's legs were two-toned, one painted in red and the other in black, emphasising polarity.

XIII

DEATH

Key Meanings
Alteration. Transformation. Loss, ending or parting of ways. Handling failure or disaster. Regeneration required. Bereavement. Recovery from illness or shock. Transition.

Wisdom
Death signals that it's time to let go and accept that a cycle has reached its end. A change may have been inevitable. It could be difficult to summon up the energy for new or difficult tasks for a while. But know that, in time, you will encounter fresh reserves and better options. What kind of support do you need to get through this shock or challenge? Follow up and set that in motion.

Colour Notes
Across recoloured versions of ancient card engravings, the reaper may appear flesh-toned, golden or with a pale blue spine.

XIV
TEMPERANCE

Key Meanings
Moderation. Self-control. Economy. Patience. Consolidation.
Harmony. Coordination. Successful combination. Friendship.
Recuperation. Time, seasons and climate.

Wisdom
Temperance signals it is time to go easy and find the path of
least resistance. If you encounter hostility, make adjustments
towards greater harmony. Make light of things. It's alright to
let go of a situation that doesn't bring fulfillment. You can
start again: find a better job, meet someone, make new friends
or quit a bad habit. Slow down and find a new approach.

Colour Notes
A fifteenth-century Italian version was coloured with egg
tempera in purple and green, and stamped with silver and
gold leaf.

XV
THE DEVIL

Key Meanings
Prophecy. Fate. Catastrophe. Downfall. Negative attitude. Temptations. Deadly sins. Obsessions. Enslavement. Bondage. Misplaced loyalty. Mystery. Magic. Astral plane experiences.

Wisdom
The Devil warns you to be careful what you're getting into and note danger signs. You may be offered something tempting, but at what price? Someone who promises the world may demand a lot back. This is a good time to notice if an addiction has taken hold. You do have the power to break free. Do something new or different, rather than repeating actions that reinforce old physical and neural pathways.

Colour Notes
Many extant early tarot decks are missing the Devil card due to religious suppression, however, it is likely that red, and darker colours like black and brown, predominated.

XVI

THE TOWER

Key Meanings
House of God. Disruption. Sudden changes. Expulsion
from earthly paradise. Divine wrath. Punishment of pride.
Losses. Rivalry that destroys. Plans ruined. Bankruptcy.
Need to start again.

Wisdom
The Tower symbolises the power to destroy, and suffering the
consequences of that. It signals the end of an era and a time
for new leadership. Pay attention to karmic developments.
Something built on the wrong basis may come tumbling
down, offering a chance to build in a better way. A situation
that worked for one party may not have worked for the other;
adjustments are necessary.

Colour Notes
In early decks the 'light' – flames, lightning or sun rays in
red, orange or yellow – conquered the 'dark', represented
by a building or tree. This may have shown the influence of
mystery plays, which emphasised moral issues.

XVII

THE STAR

Key Meanings
Hope. Bright promise. Faith. Recovery. Gifts. Symbols of immortality. Light of the spirit. Good prospects. New dawn coming. Frustrated expectations.

Wisdom
The Star heralds a time of healing, replenishment and redoubled energy. It's your moment to shine and make an impact – find a way to make your mark. Give something back, since you can provide from an overflow. Realise that the true essence of who you are is enough. Where you are frustrated, look at how you can best try again.

Colour Notes
The 1910 Rider Waite tarot deck reduced the array of yellow, blue and red stars to one yellow and seven white stars.

XVIII

THE MOON

Key Meanings
Night energy. Twilight. Reflected light. Illusion. Deception. Hidden forces. Uncertainty. Trickery. Power of feelings. Developments underground, undercover, or in the womb.

Wisdom
Something below the surface wants to emerge. You may feel resistance towards it. Feelings could be intensified, perhaps due to the time of day or night or an unusual situation. Decisions may lack clarity, so it could be best to delay action for a while. A high or low in a cycle, which will soon be quite different. If the mind has mountains, remember that you don't have to climb them – look for ways around.

Colour Notes
A 1930 reprint of the *Tarot of Marseilles* introduced stronger colours, adding a dark blue depth to the Moon's water pool.

XXI

THE WORLD

Key Meanings

Perfection. Completion. Conclusion. Reward. Prize. Long journey. The Universe, including the four seasons. The material world, supported by divine imagination. Power through intelligence and wisdom.

Wisdom

The World is about getting everything you always wanted. You may have worked hard for it or waited a long time. Now you can finally reap the rewards. You have arrived at the perfect state, where you feel untouchable and at complete peace. There are forces protecting you on all sides. Different powers or influences are coming into positive alignment. You will be supported through a coming situation.

Colour Notes

A 2006 recolouring of a 1751 Swiss deck altered the light blue, oval garland to become three segments of yellow, green and deep blue.

CUPS

WATER

Key Meanings
Love. Friendship. Family. Heartfelt involvements. Imagination. Intuition. Spirituality. Desire for fulfillment.

Colour Notes
Tarot cups, frequently golden, sometimes enamelled or bejewelled, have been depicted as chalices, goblets and the Holy Grail itself.

ACE OF CUPS

The cup overflows. An outpouring of feelings. A creative beginning. Fertility. Seeds. Pregnancy. Birth. Attraction. New relationship. Fullness. Abundance. Greatest joy. Perfection. Fulfillment.

The Ace of Cups urges us to let go of emotional baggage, find peace and live life to the full. You can begin afresh and open yourself to new relationships, whether romantic or in other spheres. Look for resonance with others and opportunities with potential to bring emotional fulfillment.

2 OF CUPS

Partnership. A harmonious match. Two hearts. A couple. Soulmate. Ability and willingness to compromise. Need to agree. Teamwork benefits. Two heads better than one.

There's a good chance of a promising relationship occurring soon. If you're already involved, the impetus is to achieve harmony so take steps to resolve any issues. In business, you gain more in team efforts than going solo. Aim to consider others before making significant moves.

3 OF CUPS

Happy gathering. Social activity. Group effort. Victory. Problems resolved. Wounds and painful memories healed. Pleasures of life. Joyous family. Support from siblings, cousins and peers. Conclusion.

It's time to extend energies toward others. Social occasions and group involvements are emphasised. There may be a cause for celebration or a project reaching a happy conclusion or a warm reception on offer. Someone can give valuable support or needs the same from you. Go with the flow!

4 OF CUPS

Preoccupation. Satiation. Aversion. Disappointment. Discontentment. Weariness. Blindness. Not seeing the good things. Isolation. Depression. Self-pity. New light. Hidden blessings.

You, or someone around you, may be feeling low or experiencing tunnel vision. Keep active and avoid isolation; get some fresh air, look at the sky, connect with trusted others and you will soon feel better. If supporting another person, take a gentle, understanding approach.

5 OF CUPS

Regret. Limited loss. Bereavement. Inheritance that is not what was anticipated. Superficial, disappointing relationships. Difficult marriage, lacking love. Bitterness spoiling good things. Possible new start.

Avoid beating yourself up over anything you had no real control over. This is the 'could have, would have, should have' syndrome – the soul's way of trying to negotiate the past. New choices and focuses can lead to a happier future; make the best available decision and move on.

6 OF CUPS

Past connections. Childhood memories. Old relationships. Joy in nostalgia. Renewal. New cycle. Harmonious networks. Positive influences. Favours earned and returned. Blessings passed on.

Present and future progress has seeds in the past. Somebody you've had a special connection with could offer an advantage soon. Where there has been animosity, pray for something better. If you have left a difficult trail anywhere, forgive yourself and focus on more positive actions.

7 OF CUPS

Nothing as it first appears. Fantasies. Pipe dreams. Unrealistic expectations. Illusions. Distorted reflections. Corruption. Premeditation. Desire. Plan. Determination. Resolution. Courage to move into real experience.

It may be challenging to make a clear choice now, so avoid putting yourself under too much pressure. What step could you take to obtain more information and gain some clarity? Remember that a situation may look quite different in the light of day, or after more time has passed.

8 OF CUPS

Limited success. Modesty. Decline. Abandoned plans. Letting go. Moving on. Something loses charge or significance. Recognising an impossible situation. Seeking new pastures.

It's time to recognise when enough is enough. You've given all you had, perhaps with limited results. An initially fruitful situation has run its course and now you need to consider a new venture, even if it feels hard to tear yourself away.

9 OF CUPS

Success and abundance, including material. Well-being. Contentment. Happy, secure future. Wholeness. Wisdom earned. Spiritual fulfillment. Trophies, rewards and other signs of achievement. Complacency. Smugness. Conceitedness.

Blow your own trumpet and give yourself a pat on the back! It's time to line up your trophies and recognise your successes. You may also be aware that you can't afford to rest on your laurels. There could be pressure, either internal or external, to continue achieving.

10 OF CUPS

Great joy. Pleasures of life. Happy family. Peace. Contentment. Ecstasy. A full heart. Being loved and cared for. Abuse and violence, if turned on its head.

It's up to you to steer life in the direction that promises the greatest happiness. Good results can come more easily to you now, especially when you feel aligned within yourself. Where a situation may have knocked you off course, you can get back on track by focusing more on positive features.

KNAVE OF CUPS

Imagination coming to life. Blonde or fair youth. Helpful. Youthful.
Effeminate. Studious, reflective, meditative. Affectionate, friendly,
charming. Deception. A potentially damaging habit or desire.

It's time to appreciate the softer, quieter side of human nature,
including your own. Give yourself more space to play and experiment,
while ensuring that what you're doing is wholesome and beneficial.
A more emotional and fulfilling connection can be developed with a
special person or interest.

KNIGHT OF CUPS

Advancing, arriving, coming on board. Reception, reconciliation.
Proposition. Invitation. Financial opportunity or windfall, often through
a visitor. Imagination, vision and passion. Cunning. Artifice. Fraud.

Imagination runs free, offering visions of a better future. You may have
good reasons for being more romantic and passionate. Now is the time
to make an advance or hold out an olive branch. Offer or accept an
invitation while being aware of other people's needs and motivations.

QUEEN OF CUPS

Blonde or fair woman. Mature. Honest. Devoted, faithful wife, good mother and friend. Wise visionary. Actions help a dream become real. Pleasure. Happiness. Service. Success.

Emotional honesty and support speak volumes and can work in your favour. An opportunity may present itself to benefit from the greater wisdom and kindness of a feminine personality. Focus on comforts you can extend to others and gentle pastimes that bring you peace and pleasure.

KING OF CUPS

Fair or blonde, older male. Responsible, honest, kind man. Creative, educated or professional. Liberal, poetic, artistic. Religious, lawman or businessman. Fluctuating, unreliable, lacking persistence.

It's time to do the right thing by others, recognising the merits of honesty, perseverance and sheer hard work. It may be tempting to give up on a project because you doubt your ability, but dedication and tenacity will build greater confidence. Harness belief and look for creative solutions.

SWORDS

AIR

Key Meanings
Worry. Illness. Trouble and strife. The power of
words. Truth. Fairness. Objectivity. Boundaries.

Colour Notes
Sword styles include rapiers, sabres, scimitars,
cutlasses – shaded silver and gold; or black and
red, echoing risks of injury.

ACE OF SWORDS

---

*Truth. Courage. Vision. Insight. Power. Triumph. Accomplishment.
Irresistible force. Cutting through to the heart of the matter. On a roll.
Needed change.*

The truth will set you free. You possess the power to cut to the core
of thorny issues and the ability to move forward with greater courage
and conviction. While confronting raw truth may be painful, it can
also arm you with valuable, powerful clarity.

2 OF SWORDS

Stalemate. Conformity. Inner conflict. Duplicity. Disloyalty. Desire for respite. Truce. Poise. Balance of opposing parts.

It can be much harder to move forward when you feel divided, or when you're afraid of the outcome. Ask yourself if you're ready yet. If the answer is no, is this to do with temporary circumstances or do you need to make a change? Protection may be your priority.

3 OF SWORDS

Disruptive forces. Incompatibility. Heartache. Distance. Absence. Alienation. Unrest. Confusion. Delay. Loss of bearings. Loss of moral compass. Resolving a moral dilemma. Victory through right action. The healing power of pure intentions. No pain, no gain.

You may feel unbalanced by a recent development, triggering difficult thoughts and feelings. Remember that these may be temporary, and you may not know the whole story. Time will help you deal with any pain or unravel a puzzling situation. Focus on what will lessen the impact.

4 OF SWORDS

Mental security. Retreat. Rest. Peace. Practical spirit. Good organisation of ideas. Limitations of rational thought. Scientific rigidity.

It's time to let go of usual responsibilities, if only for a short while. Give yourself space and peace so you may reconnect with your inner self. If you're working on a critical project, standing back may help you gain a clearer view. Take time to prepare carefully for important conversations.

5 OF SWORDS

Greater self-knowledge, often from mistakes and hardship. Brute force, sometimes with destructive consequences. Strength through persistence vs. over-ambition. Possible losses through acting purely in your own interests.

Maintaining stamina and momentum may be helpful, but be wary of trying to force an outcome. You may know what you want personally, but a compromise may be the best way forward. Carefully consider all the possible consequences of both planned and more impetuous actions.

6 OF SWORDS

Journey. Going to warmer (or cooler) climes. Messenger. Kind attention. Success after trials. Recovery from illness or bereavement.

Life wants to send you along smoother waters. Where there has been stress, calmer times are due to follow. Allow others to assist you through any rough patches; things will get easier. Where any tension still persists, ask yourself what steps you can take to begin to defuse it.

7 OF SWORDS

Cunning. Skillfulness and determination that need to be used for the right purposes. Considering escape from an imprisoning situation. Manipulation that tends to backfire. Watch your back. Change of heart. Treachery.

You may be tempted to leave a set of circumstances that don't feel quite right, but leaving might not be straightforward. Some sort of middle path could seem to make more sense. Check whether concealed activity that takes extra energy to manage is worthwhile.

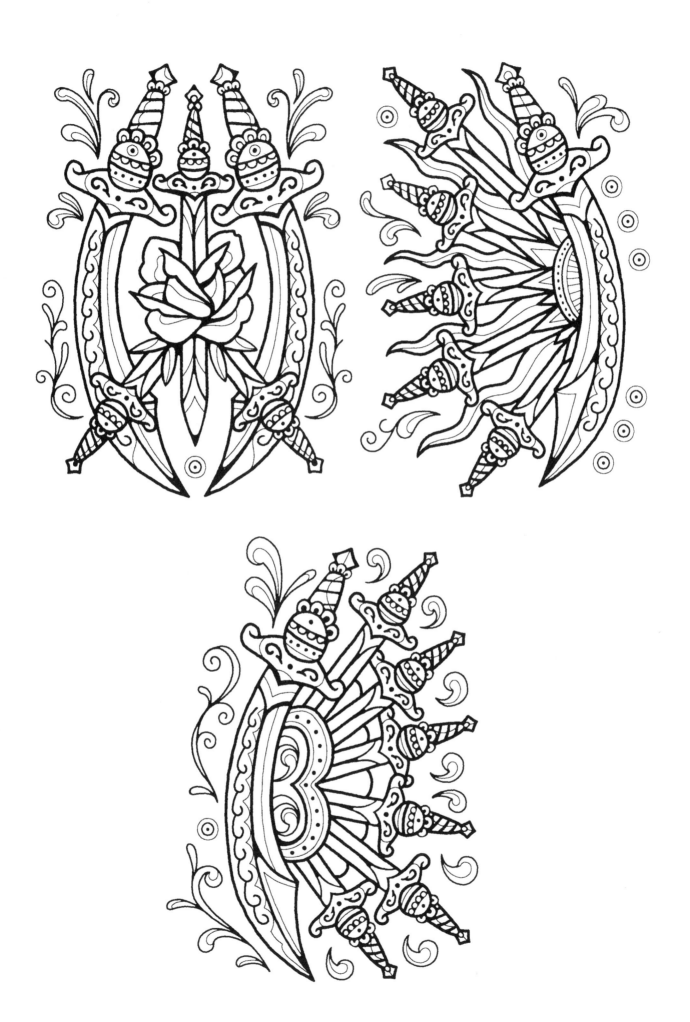

8 OF SWORDS

Contradiction. Criticism. Reprimand. Crisis. Temporary difficulties. Blame. Censure. Scandal. Trauma that can be healed. Swamped by details. Being trapped. A dark night of the soul. The mental void and paralysis created through fear. Beliefs and thoughts that can be changed.

You may feel cornered, currently, but this does not have to be forever. The power of fear can keep you pinned in one place, unable to see options. Do what you can to reduce any pressure or anxiety and you will move closer to a new opportunity.

9 OF SWORDS

Power of the mind. Third eye. Good faith, integrity. Busy mind. Suspicion. Fear. Despair. Shame. Misery. Anxiety regarding loved ones. Hermit. Meditation. Sanctuary. Ceremony. Ritual.

When we let thoughts escalate, it's easy to perceive a situation as far worse than it really is. Your challenge now is to dismantle fear, worry, and any tendency to focus on catastrophe. Figure out why you're experiencing these feelings and work out how to encourage greater calm.

10 OF SWORDS

Affliction. Sadness. Grief. Pain. Grievances. We can let things drag us down or let the negative thoughts and feelings go, pick ourselves up, and move on. Faith in difficult circumstances. It's only a matter of time and choice before the page can be turned.

There are times we cannot deny that things are rough and it's hard to imagine them being better, but better they will be! It may take a while to get over a tough ordeal or setback, but you just have to wait it out until the tide turns. Keep the faith.

KNAVE OF SWORDS

Spy. Observer. Intelligence. Vigilance. Examination. Indiscretion. Surprise. The unknown, unseen, and unexpected. Stealth. Cunning. Outspoken, sometimes at cost, but skillful at handling controversy.

Expect the unexpected — you might feel you need eyes in the back of your head for a while. Look at everything more closely, collect facts and be analytical. Picking up on small details can offer an advantage, so long as you keep them to yourself.

KNIGHT OF SWORDS

Dashing, brave, potent defender. Expert soldier and marksman. Skillful, practiced. Astute. Attacking. Starts battles. Courageous hero. Prompts action. Nips in the bud. Recklessness. Impulsive errors. Indiscretion.

Someone is up for a fight! Don't approach without preparation. If you need to take someone to task, you'll benefit from arranging your strategy ahead. Where circumstances force you to think on the spot, draw on existing wisdom. Where anyone is baiting, you have a choice.

QUEEN OF SWORDS

Tough exterior with inner fragility or coldness. Fault-finding.
Belittling. Experiencing hardship. Widow. Barren. Sterile. Mourning.
Separation. Loneliness. Famine. Losses and their effects.
Nasty attitude. Slander.

One mean woman, but with grounds for her hardness, this queen has
been through painful times and doesn't let people in easily. You may
feel alone or lonely, although there is support around if you're willing
to let your guard down. Remember, many people do mean well.

KING OF SWORDS

Businessman. Judge. Lawyer. Doctor. Adviser. Authority. Power.
Superiority. Experience. Justice and fairness. Military intelligence.
Analytical. Fixed opinions. Controlling nature. Dictator. Ruthless.
Conflict. Barbarity.

Draw on the wisdom of your accumulated experience. Your next
move merits extra thought; remember success with previous strategies.
You can be a tough defender but a fair attitude may attract optimum
results. Be wary of crossing someone. Instead, evaluate various options
to find the best way forward.

WANDS

FIRE

Key Meanings
Spontaneity. Fast action. Passion. Power. Adrenaline. Life force. Creative fuel and urges. Inspired work. Stroke of genius.

Colour Notes
Wands or batons, based on historic Egyptian polo sticks, had coloured sections in various combinations of red, yellow and blue.

ACE OF WANDS

Birth. Force. Primary energy. Vigour. Vitality. Creativity. New enterprise. First fruits. Family origins. Progress. Invention. Dramatic impact. Release of energy. Initiative. Aiming high. Extremism.

An energy surge as life force and drive increase. This is a chance to create something new: a baby, structure or special project. Focus on what you're most passionate about. Now is the time to allow the inner flame of desire to arise in a productive way that reflects life's positive magic.

2 OF WANDS

Individual success vs. codependency. Restlessness, boredom. Dissatisfaction with current lot. Seeking greener pastures. Restraint. Getting needs met. Temporary need for independence. To stay or go?

You may be at cross-purposes. Is someone else holding you back? Are you clinging on to a situation that has lost its lustre? You deserve more. Allow yourself the freedom to explore other pastures, even if only to appreciate what is out there compared to what you already have.

3 OF WANDS

Strength in numbers. Business cooperation and success. Busy times. Being on the go. Established strength. Troubles ending. Ceasefire. Ship coming in. Mixed loyalties. Occasional disappointments.

It's time to use a network to help expand your interests. Take steps to make sure you're kept in the loop and don't miss out. Be ready to be busier, to help create more of what you want. Where you've already put in efforts, you could soon see thrilling rewards.

4 OF WANDS

Peace and rest. Holiday. Celebration. Job well done. Happy home life. Joyful outcome, or waiting for a conclusion. Harmony. Beauty. Love is in the air.

Grab your glad rags, it's time to party! There should be good news soon. Something is nearing a satisfactory completion. A glamorous social or business opportunity can open the door to love. Conversely, a positive connection with someone can lead to good business progression.

5 OF WANDS

Competition. Battle for life and success. Play-acting. Conflicting opinions, ambitions or activities. Too many choices. Needing to accommodate varied tastes and needs. Complexity. Struggle.

Are too many cooks spoiling the broth? It may be that you and those around you all have good ideas, but there's not quite enough room now for them to coexist harmoniously. Respect each other's talents and focus on doing your own thing wherever you can make a positive impact.

6 OF WANDS

Good news. Well-earned victory. Hopes and expectations fulfilled. Public honours. Success that builds future success. Honest discussion needed where there has been doubt or apprehension.

Get ready to hold your head high — great success is within reach! You have earned respect for your efforts so take the compliments, believe in yourself and recognise your contribution. It's time to conquer other people's fears by showing confidence and opening up the conversation.

7 OF WANDS

Resolute firmness and bravery. Overcoming challenges, even if outwardly against the odds. Winning through fighting from a position of advantage. The strength of personal integrity.

You've reached a stage when other people see you as a force to contend with. Be ready to stand your ground, including refusing to open doors to anyone who could bring too much trouble. Remain true to yourself. Allow sufficient time to study the situation and develop a sound strategy.

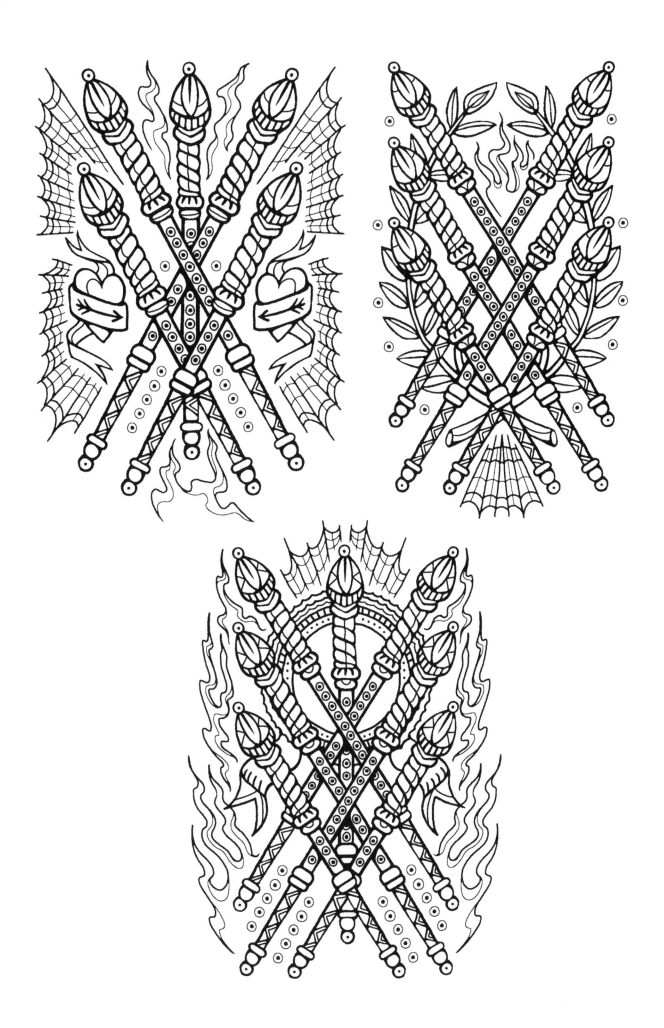

8 OF WANDS

Progress. Breakthrough. Events moving quickly. On the threshold of something new. Promises or proposals. Object of desire or envy. Hasty decisions and actions. Quarrels. Harassment.

Where something isn't working, let go and focus your energy elsewhere. Matters will progress fast! You may be juggling several projects at once, but keep your eyes on the prize. If your feet barely touch the ground, it may be because life has found natural ways to carry you forward.

9 OF WANDS

Stamina, discipline. Strength in adversity. Good powers of recovery and healing after injury, accident or illness. Preparing well ahead. Managing delays. Success after a setback.

It's time to rally the forces, both internally and externally. You may feel tired after a lot of effort, with yet more to be done. Hang in there and look for some long-term support. Foresight will tend to pay dividends, whereas ignoring warning signs will not.

10 OF WANDS

Success and honours, but at a price. Fulfilling obligations whilst oppressed by their weight. Striving towards deadlines. Climbing a precarious ladder. Needing to reduce pressure.

Has martyr syndrome taken hold? Hitting rock bottom may make you feel victimised by behaviours or circumstances. Either way, know that you've likely reached the lowest point; aim to simply rest and conserve energy ready for a move upwards and outwards to a better situation.

KNAVE OF WANDS

News and announcements. Messages arriving. Dark youth. Courageous. Loyal friend. Decent character. Person to be trusted. Inherited intelligence and skills. Instability. Reluctance. Indecision or rash choices.

Useful information is on the way, heralding a new development. This fiery knave has access to divine inspiration and can deliver great ideas that should be acted upon. Whilst speed may be of the essence, a moment's thought for appropriateness before speaking or acting is probably also wise.

KNIGHT OF WANDS

On the move. Travel, flight, departure. Disruption. Altered plans. Home modifications. New address. Moving abroad. Absence. Away from home. Stranger's arrival upsetting the status quo.

Time to get going, with or without much preparation. Great motivation and impetus can help kick-start a domestic, professional or personal project. Adrenaline is pumping and prompt action is required. Prepare for someone ignoring the opinions or feelings of others, probably through a lack of time and a disregard for niceties.

QUEEN OF WANDS

Lady of the manor. Charming, magnetic and friendly. Loving. Honorable. Understanding, sympathetic and practical. Likes money, but understands economy. Snobbery. Obstinacy. Deceit. Social introductions. Business success.

She is the 'hostess with the mostest' and we all want to be her friend! The ability to put on a show and make others feel welcome brings an opportunity to make some useful connections. Grandeur may make some people feel they're lacking or excluded, if handled wrongly.

KING OF WANDS

Estate owner or manager. Wise. Conscientious. Educated. Pillar of the community. Good mediator. Devoted and loyal. Good conscience. Can be strict and harsh. Severe measures. Austerity.

Become more of an authority, going by the book and acting appropriately, whilst having a heart. Draw on your natural charisma and effective communication skills. It's time to consult with the head person and make connections that can help with moving up a notch. Avoid becoming too fierce or intense.

COINS

EARTH

Key Meanings
Slow and considered activity. Solid growth.
Money matters. Material interests. Buildings.
Possessions. Paid work. Profit. Business. Labour.

Colour Notes
Tarot coins have classically been coloured in a
mix of yellow and black, producing an effect
similar to used currency.

ACE OF COINS

---

*Treasure. Riches. Prosperity. Attainment. Recognition. Contentment.
Fulfillment. May relate to work, pregnancy or childbirth. Triumph.
Profit. Security and its price. Fresh financial start. New enterprise.*

This could mark a business proposal or initiative that will bring a new
financial chapter. Begin to build resources and convert materials or
assets into another form. It's time to put your talents to good use! Start
developing a skill, get a commercial or charitable idea off the ground
or volunteer. Take the first step to make it happen!

2 OF COINS

Flow of money (in or out). Obtaining money to survive. A happy 'business' face. Getting what you pay for. Energy fluctuations. Ongoing work to launch an enterprise.

It's all about checks and balances and keeping a cash flow situation going. What goes around comes around, and what you put in comes back to you, if it's meant to. A good time to weigh up options and make sure your energy is going into the right channels for the results you want.

3 OF COINS

Mastery, skill and accomplishment. Good reputation in work or business. Expertise built on experience. Craftsmanship. High status. Honours earned. Negatively: average or low quality, lack of funding.

You're in demand! Gold stars are well deserved. Where you've left a good impression, it should start to pay off. High ratings mean your reputation goes before you. Be confident and focus on the job at hand. Don't let perfectionism block the energy to keep to schedules.

4 OF COINS

Inheritance. Gift, win, grant or benefit. Status through wealth. Financial protection and security. Insurance. Fear of destitution and loss. Meanness. The comfort-zone trap. Hoarding.

You may be able to secure your position, but try not to allow complacency, possessiveness, stagnancy or distrust to take over. Remember life's natural systems of flow. In giving a little, you may gain something back. It could make sense to actively work on purposeful savings; greed should not govern.

5 OF COINS

Material struggle, whether related to work issues, health problems, overspending, partnership or family loyalties. Loss. Disadvantage. Recovery from ruin. Potential to reverse a bad trend.

Where a situation is not ideal, do not give up hope. A turning point suggests that one step in a new, or better, direction could improve matters. Ask for assistance in the right place. You may need to trust that you could be helped and open a door to positive developments.

6 OF COINS

Good financial trend. On the up-and-up. Caring acts. Generosity. Charity. Benefactor. Paying attention. Being vigilant. Desire. Illusion. Envy or jealousy. Paying debts or bail.

Kindness doesn't only help others; it can also make you feel happier. Be willing to give, but without strings attached, as generosity laced with expectations can backfire. Someone may be able to assist you without requiring anything back. It is valuable to work on clearing the slate, wherever possible.

7 OF COINS

Profit, growth and progress. Valuable assets. Fruits of labour. Hard toil. On a learning curve. Anxiety around money. Potential for improved status or work promotion.

Giving a situation time to develop can be important, especially where business and money are concerned. Practical circumstances may dictate just how long you can allow, and how much effort you can extend, before solid results need to become the norm. One more push may be all that's needed.

8 OF COINS

Apprenticeship. Employment. Commission. Craftsmanship. Planning and preparing. Skillful. Calculating. Ambition, or a lack of ambition. Backroom work. Community role. Loans, advances, interest and repayment terms.

Fresh eyes on a situation can bring a beneficial new energy to it. It's a good time for learning and trying out new skills, taking in information and developing a stronger understanding. Trust your insights and learn from any mistakes, as they too hold value. Map out your next move and rehearse well.

9 OF COINS

Material comfort. Abundance. Wanting for little. Accomplishment. Honours. Gains. Sense of self-worth. Safety and security. Prudence. Long-term planning. Managing danger. Able to weather a storm.

There should be enough spare, one way or another, to allow for a few more comforts. Where there has been scarcity, however, it's time to plan in building some cushioning for the future. Let there be scope in your agenda to enjoy nature's abundance and the simple pleasures of life.

10 OF COINS

Wealth. Security. Prosperity. Gain. The height of success. Family matters. Generations. Posterity. Archives. Family residence. Lodging. Den. Domestic economics. Savings. Dowry. Pension. Sustainable losses. Gambling.

You've scooped the jackpot and unlocked the code for success. Reach a level of earning or sustainability where the living is easy and rewards keep coming. It's time to look at the bigger picture and aim high. Consider the passing on of treasures and values to loved ones.

KNAVE OF COINS

Study. Reflection. Meditation. Concentration. Application. Rule. Instruction. Scholarship. Love of learning and knowledge. Messenger. Collecting and circulating information. Management, or its lack. Liberal. Luxury. Wasteful.

The perfect time to consider the best use of resources. Quiet reflection brings answers to practical problems. How can you expand your knowledge base? What can be learned now? Play according to the rules and remain grounded, taking initial, concrete steps forward. A few little luxuries can bring pleasure and satisfaction.

KNIGHT OF COINS

Trustworthy and brave man. Methodical. Reliability. Responsibility. Decency. Perseverance. Patience. Able to finish the task. What is necessary. Profitable. Interest. Spare time. Unemployment. Idleness. Inertia. Stagnation.

You want something or someone to rely on. The dependable one who starts slowly usually gets there in the end. Don't try to rush without a sound reason. This is a signal to take your time and do something properly. When you need to combat apathy, lethargy or procrastination, just do the next right thing.

QUEEN OF COINS

Dark woman. Opulence. Generosity. Riches. Luxury. Pomp. Security. Assurance. Dignity, Well-being. Abundance. Grace. Liberty. Indecisive. Indiscretion. Suspicion. Doubt. Suspense. Terror. Viciousness. Neglectful of responsibilities. Illness.

The well turned-out one who invests in the good stuff. A sign to look after grooming and make sure you go the extra mile. Appearances will tend to count more now, so work on making a good impression. In your private space, you can relax and be yourself. Look after physical comforts.

KING OF COINS

Dark man. Characterful person. Master. Successful. Valour. Victory. Bravery. Experienced. Intelligent. Business acumen. Geometry. Physics. Defect. Danger. Weakness. Imperfection. Corruption. Vice. Perversity.

Become a financial kingpin. Order and planning make sense so keep track of the books or find someone with a brain for figures. It's time to handle practicalities and responsibilities, while remembering to smell the coffee and enjoy the view. You have a body and spirit for enjoying life, so maintain them well.

Oliver Munden, also known as MEGAMUNDEN, has turned his hand to all manner of styles and applications, from large-scale murals and retail interiors to record covers, paper and skin. Vintage skate art, psychedelia, renaissance art and, most notably, European, American and Japanese tattoo aesthetics are combined to create a signature style which attracts both private and commercial clients. Oliver works as a tattooist at Rock Steady Tattoo on the south coast of England, as well as taking on commercial artwork projects. Find more of his work at megamunden.com.

Diana McMahon Collis has studied and practiced tarot for over 30 years and, in 2001, co-founded the Tarot Association of the British Isles. She has provided tarot talks and client readings as a consultant at Champneys Forest Mere Health Resort, and offers a professional astrology/tarot email reading service via her website mindbliss.co.uk and the Circle of Professional Clairvoyants. She has written articles, columns and tarot book and deck reviews for a wide range of outlets and has collaborated on several books.

ALSO AVAILABLE

THE TATTOO COLOURING BOOK
£9.99
978 1 78067 012 6

THE TATTOO FLASH COLOURING BOOK
£12.99
978 1 78067 916 7

TATTOO TAROT
£14.99
978 1 78627 205 8